Duck! and The Rainbow Room

'Duck!' and 'The Rainbow Room'
An original concept by Jenny Jinks
© Jenny Jinks

Illustrated by Patricia Pessoa

Published by MAVERICK ARTS PUBLISHING LTD
Studio 11, City Business Centre, 6 Brighton Road,
Horsham, West Sussex, RH13 5BB
© Maverick Arts Publishing Limited February 2020
+44 (0)1403 256941

A CIP catalogue record for this book is available at the British Library.

ISBN 978-1-84886-652-2

publishing

www.maverickbooks.co.uk

This book is rated as: Red Band (Guided Reading)
This story is mostly decodable at Letters and Sounds Phase 3.
Up to eight non-decodable story words are included.

Duck! and The Rainbow Room

By **Jenny Jinks**

Illustrated by
Patricia Pessoa

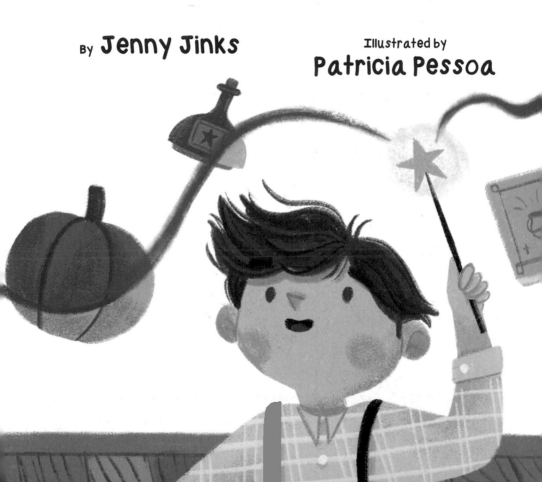

The Letter D

Trace the lower and upper case letter with a finger. Sound out the letter.

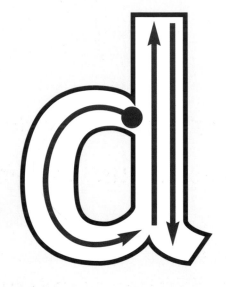

Around,
up,
down

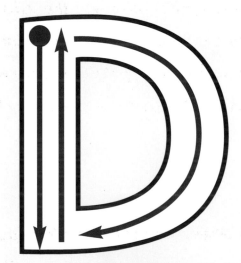

Down,
up,
around

Some words to familiarise:

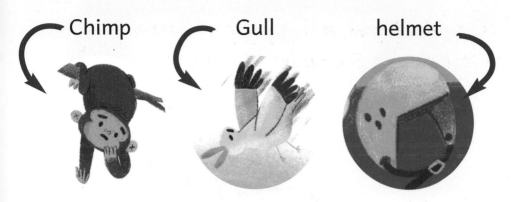

Chimp

Gull

helmet

High-frequency words:

said was to up we you it a

Tips for Reading 'Duck!'

- Practise the words listed above before reading the story.

- If the reader struggles with any of the other words, ask them to look for sounds they know in the word. Encourage them to sound out the words and help them read the words if necessary.

- After reading the story, ask the reader why Duck kept getting hit.

Fun Activity

Think of some other presents that could help Duck.

Duck!

"Duck!" said Chimp.
Pam and Tad ducked.

But Duck did not.
"Yes?" said Duck.

BANG!

"Duck!" said Gull.
Pam and Tad ducked.

But Duck did not. "Yes?"

BANG!

"Duck!" said Frog.
Pam and Tad ducked.

But Duck did not.
"Yes?"

BANG!

Duck was fed up.

He went back to bed.

"Duck!"
But Duck did not get up.

"Duck! Duck!" said Pam and Tad.
"We got you this!"

It was a helmet.

"Thank you!" said Duck.

The Letter R

Trace the lower and upper case letter with a finger. Sound out the letter.

*Down,
up,
around*

*Down,
up,
around,
down*

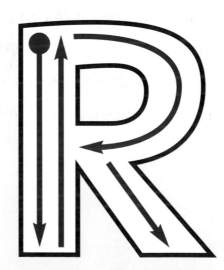

Some words to familiarise:

Nak   Tig   Gus

High-frequency words:

is my said I it a was they the

Tips for Reading 'The Rainbow Room'

- Practise the words listed above before reading the story.

- If the reader struggles with any of the other words, ask them to look for sounds they know in the word. Encourage them to sound out the words and help them read the words if necessary.

- After reading the story, ask the reader why the rainbow room was the best.

Fun Activity

Discuss your favourite colours.

The Rainbow Room

"This is my room," said Nak.
"I will turn it red."

Zip!

"No. This is my room," said Tig.
"I will turn it blue."

Zap!

"No. This is my room," said Gus.
"I will turn it pink."

Zop!

"RED!" said Nak.

"BLUE!" said Tig.

"PINK!" said Gus.

Zip! Zap! Zop!

"STOP!" said Mum.

"This room is a mess!"

It was red.

And blue.

And pink.

"It is perfect!" they said.

"This room is the best!"

Book Bands for Guided Reading

The Institute of Education book banding system is a scale of colours that reflects the various levels of reading difficulty. The bands are assigned by taking into account the content, the language style, the layout and phonics. Word, phrase and sentence level work is also taken into consideration.

Maverick Early Readers are a bright, attractive range of books covering the pink to white bands. All of these books have been book banded for guided reading to the industry standard and edited by a leading educational consultant.

Pink
Red
Yellow
Blue
Green
Orange
Turquoise
Purple
Gold
White

To view the whole Maverick Readers scheme, visit our website at
www.maverickearlyreaders.com

Or scan the QR code above to view our scheme instantly!